SCHUBERT

SONATA

in A minor

"Arpeggione"

FOR VIOLA AND PIANO

(MILTON KATIMS)

INTERNATIONAL MUSIC COMPANY
NEW YORK 10017

SONATA

Viola part edited by *MILTON KATIMS*
Cello part edited by *LEONARD ROSE*

FRANZ SCHUBERT
(1797-1828)

Arpeggione *)
or Viola or Cello
or Violin

PIANO

Allegro moderato

*) A stringed instrument of the size of a cello, with a guitar-like body and played with a bow;
invented in 1823 by G. Staufer and now obsolete.

4

8

320

12

320

20

320

VIOLA MUSIC

VIOLA SOLO

BACH, Johann Sebastian
Six Cello Suites *(KATIMS)*
Six Violin Sonatas and Partitas *(MEYER-VIELAND)*

BEETHOVEN, Ludwig van
Viola part for the Six Celebrated Piano
  Trios *(to replace the Cello) (ALTMANN)*

BLUMENSTENGEL, A.
Op. 33. 24 Studies *(WIEMANN)*

BORISSOVSKY, Vadim
Four Artistic Studies

BRAHMS, Johannes
Viola part for the Double Concerto, Op. 102
  (to replace the Cello) (VIELAND)

BRUNI, Antoine-Barthelemy
25 Studies *(SCHULZ)*

CAMPAGNOLI, Bartolomeo
Op. 22. 41 Caprices *(PRIMROSE)*

DANCLA, Charles
Op. 74. School of Mechanism *(VIELAND)*

DONT, Jacob
Op. 37. 24 Studies *(preparatory to Kreutzer
  and Rode Studies) (VIELAND)*

FIORILLO, Federigo
31 Selected Studies *(VIELAND)*

FUCHS, Lillian
16 Fantasy Etudes

GAVINIES, Pierre
24 Studies *(SPITZNER)*

HERMANN, Friedrich
Op. 18. Six Concert Studies
Op. 22. Technical Studies

HOFFMEISTER, Franz Anton
Twelve Studies *(C. HERRMANN)*

HOFMANN, Richard
Op. 86. First Studies (in the 1st Position)
Op. 87. 15 Studies

KAYSER, Heinrich Ernst
Op. 20. 36 Studies *(VIELAND)*
Op. 43. 36 Studies
Op. 55. 24 Studies

KREUTZER, Rodolphe
42 Studies *(PAGELS)*

MAYSEDER, Joseph
Op. 29. Six Etudes *(PAGELS)*

MAZAS, Jacques Féréol
Op. 36. Bk. I. Etudes Spéciales *(PAGELS)*
Op. 36. Bk. II. Etudes Brillantes *(PAGELS)*

ORCHESTRAL EXCERPTS *(see VIELAND)*

PAGANINI, Niccolo
Op. 1. 24 Caprices *(RABY)*

VIOLA SOLO (cont'd)

PALASCHKO, Johannes
Op. 36. Twenty Studies
Op. 49. Ten Studies
Op. 55. Twelve Studies

REGER, Max
Op. 131d. Three Suites

RODE, Pierre
24 Caprices *(PAGELS)*

ROVELLI, Pietro
Op. 3 & Op. 5. 12 Caprices *(PAGELS)*

SCHRADIECK, Henri
School of Viola Technique:
  Volume I *(PAGELS)*
  Volume II *(PAGELS)*
  Volume III *(PAGELS)*

STRAUSS, Richard
Orchestral Excerpts *(VIELAND)*

(List of contents on request)

VIELAND, Joseph
Orchestral Excerpts from Classical & Modern Works
  covering a wide range of Symphonic Repertoire.
  (from BACH to RAVEL and STRAVINSKY):
  Volume I
  Volume II
  Volume III
  Volume IV
  Volume V

(List of contents on request)

WAGNER, Richard
Orchestral Excerpts *(VIELAND)*
(List of contents on request)

WOHLFAHRT, Franz
Op. 45, 60 Studies
  Volume I *(VIELAND)*
  Volume II *(VIELAND)*

TWO VIOLAS

BACH, Wilhelm Friedemann
Three Duets

MAZAS, Jacques-Féréol
Op. 71. Three Duets. *(PAGELS)*

PLEYEL, Ignace
Op. 8. Three Duets *(PAASCH)*

TELEMANN, Georg Philipp
Six Canonic Sonatas *(DAVIS)*

INTERNATIONAL MUSIC COMPANY

545 FIFTH AVENUE

Complete catalog sent free on request

NEW YORK 10017

No. 45-83

VIOLA MUSIC

VIOLA SOLO

BACH, Johann Sebastian
Six Cello Suites (KATIMS)
Six Violin Sonatas and Partitas (MEYER-VIELAND)

BEETHOVEN, Ludwig van
Viola part for the Six Celebrated Piano
  Trios (to replace the Cello) (ALTMANN)

BLUMENSTENGEL, A.
Op. 33. 24 Studies (WIEMANN)

BORISSOVSKY, Vadim
Four Artistic Studies

BRAHMS, Johannes
Viola part for the Double Concerto, Op. 102
  (to replace the Cello) (VIELAND)

BRUNI, Antoine-Barthelemy
25 Studies (SCHULZ)

CAMPAGNOLI, Bartolomeo
Op. 22. 41 Caprices (PRIMROSE)

DANCLA, Charles
Op. 74. School of Mechanism (VIELAND)

DONT, Jacob
Op. 37. 24 Studies (preparatory to Kreutzer
  and Rode Studies) (VIELAND)

FIORILLO, Federigo
31 Selected Studies (VIELAND)

FUCHS, Lillian
16 Fantasy Etudes

GAVINIES, Pierre
24 Studies (SPITZNER)

HERMANN, Friedrich
Op. 18. Six Concert Studies
Op. 22. Technical Studies

HOFFMEISTER, Franz Anton
Twelve Studies (C. HERRMANN)

HOFMANN, Richard
Op. 86. First Studies (in the 1st Position)
Op. 87. 15 Studies

KAYSER, Heinrich Ernst
Op. 20. 36 Studies (VIELAND)
Op. 43. 36 Studies
Op. 55. 24 Studies

KREUTZER, Rodolphe
42 Studies (PAGELS)

MAYSEDER, Joseph
Op. 29. Six Etudes (PAGELS)

MAZAS, Jacques Féréol
Op. 36. Bk. I. Etudes Spéciales (PAGELS)
Op. 36. Bk. II. Etudes Brillantes (PAGELS)

ORCHESTRAL EXCERPTS (see VIELAND)

PAGANINI, Niccolo
Op. 1. 24 Caprices (RABY)

VIOLA SOLO (cont'd)

PALASCHKO, Johannes
Op. 36. Twenty Studies
Op. 49. Ten Studies
Op. 55. Twelve Studies

REGER, Max
Op. 131d. Three Suites

RODE, Pierre
24 Caprices (PAGELS)

ROVELLI, Pietro
Op. 3 & Op. 5. 12 Caprices (PAGELS)

SCHRADIECK, Henri
School of Viola Technique:
  Volume I (PAGELS)
  Volume II (PAGELS)
  Volume III (PAGELS)

STRAUSS, Richard
Orchestral Excerpts (VIELAND)

  (List of contents on request)

VIELAND, Joseph
Orchestral Excerpts from Classical & Modern Works
  covering a wide range of Symphonic Repertoire.
  (from BACH to RAVEL and STRAVINSKY):
  Volume I
  Volume II
  Volume III
  Volume IV
  Volume V

  (List of contents on request)

WAGNER, Richard
Orchestral Excerpts (VIELAND)
  (List of contents on request)

WOHLFAHRT, Franz
Op. 45. 60 Studies
  Volume I (VIELAND)
  Volume II (VIELAND)

TWO VIOLAS

BACH, Wilhelm Friedemann
Three Duets

MAZAS, Jacques-Féréol
Op. 71. Three Duets. (PAGELS)

PLEYEL, Ignace
Op. 8. Three Duets (PAASCH)

TELEMANN, Georg Philipp
Six Canonic Sonatas (DAVIS)

INTERNATIONAL MUSIC COMPANY
545 FIFTH AVENUE
Complete catalog sent free on request
NEW YORK 10017

No. 45-83